Level 2

FAVORITE MELODIES
THE WORLD OVER

arranged by Jane Smisor Bastien

The Bastien Older Beginner Piano Library

PREFACE

FAVORITE MELODIES THE WORLD OVER, LEVEL 2 is designed to supplement **THE OLDER BEGINNER PIANO COURSE, LEVEL 2.** However, this volume may be used as supplementary enrichment with any piano course. The timeless appeal of the well-known melodies will provide hours of enjoyment for the pianist and listener.

Suggested Use of Materials with the **OLDER BEGINNER PIANO COURSE, LEVEL 2**

When the student reaches **page 5,** he is ready to begin .... **Musicianship, Level 2** (WP35)
When the student reaches **page 21,** he is ready to begin .... **Favorite Melodies the World Over, Level 2** (WP38)
When the student reaches **page 37,** he is ready to begin .... **Pop, Rock 'n Blues, Book 2** (GP38)
When the student reaches **page 45,** he is ready to begin .... **Scott Joplin Favorites** (GP90)

Published by Kjos West.
Distributed by Neil A. Kjos Music Company.
National Order Desk, 4382 Jutland Dr., San Diego, CA 92117

ISBN 0-8497-5035-0
Cover Photo: Harry Crosby/Photophile

CONTENTS

CLASSIFIED INDEX

OLD FAVORITES

In My Merry Oldsmobile

VINCENT BRYAN

GUS EDWARDS

Home On the Range

COWBOY SONG

Oh, give me a home where the buf - fa - lo roam, Where the

deer and the an - te - lope play. _____ Where

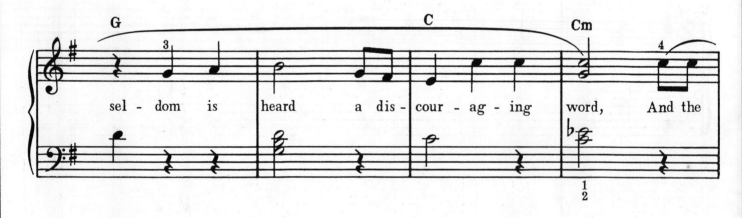

sel - dom is heard a dis - cour - ag - ing word, And the

skies are not cloud - y all day. _____

Sweet Betsy from Pike

WESTERN FOLK SONG

Did you ev-er hear of Sweet Bet-sy from Pike, Who

crossed the wide prai-ries with her lov-er Ike, With

two yoke of ox-en, a big yel-low dog, A ___

tall Shang-hai roost-er and one spot-ted hog? Sing-in'

too-ra-li-oo-ra-li-oo-ra-li-ay.

Old Black Joe

STEPHEN FOSTER

The Band Played On

JOHN F. PALMER

CHARLES B. WARD

Turkey in the Straw

AMERICAN FOLK SONG

Lively

She'll Be Comin' 'Round the Mountain

SOUTHERN MOUNTAIN SONG

Dixie

DAN D. EMMETT

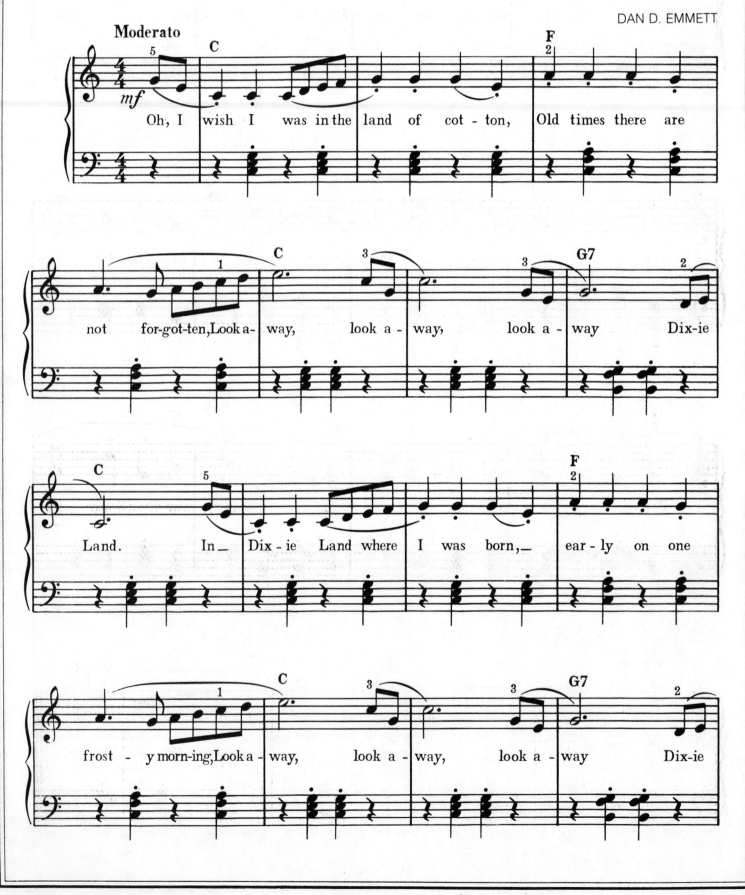

Home, Sweet Home

JOHN HOWARD PAYNE   HENRY BISHOP

'Mid plea - sures and pal - a - ces tho'— we may roam, Be it

ev - er so hum - ble, there's no — place like home. A

charm — from the skies seems to hal - low us there, which

seek — thro' the world is ne'er met — with else - where. Home, home —

sweet, sweet home, Be it ev - er so hum - ble, there's no — place like home.

Hello! My Baby

HOWARD

EMERSON

My Old Kentucky Home

The sun shines bright on my old Ken-tuck-y home, 'Tis sum-mer, the old folks are gay; The corn-top's ripe and the mead-ow's in the bloom, While the birds make mu-sic all the day. The

Country Gardens

ENGLISH DANCE

CHRISTMAS CAROLS

O Come All Ye Faithful

F. OAKELEY

J. READING

Silent Night

JOSEPH MÖHR

FRANZ GRUBER

WP38

Joy To the World

ISAAC WATTS

GEORGE F. HANDEL

O Christmas Tree

Moderato

GERMAN CAROL

It Came Upon a Midnight Clear

EDMUND H. SEARS

RICHARD S. WILLIS

God Rest Ye Merry, Gentlemen

TRADITIONAL

Moderato

Hark! the Herald Angels Sing

CHARLES WESLEY

FELIX MENDELSSOHN

O Little Town of Bethlehem

PHILLIPS BROOKS

LEWIS H. REDNER

Deck the Halls

OLD WELSH AIR

With spirit

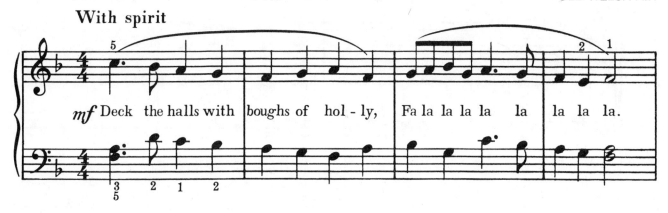

mf Deck the halls with boughs of hol - ly, Fa la la la la la la la la.

'Tis the sea - son to be jol - ly, Fa la la la la la la la la.

Don we now our gay ap-pa - rel Fa la la la la la la la la.

Troll the an - cient Yule-tide car - ol Fa la la la la la la la la.

What Child Is This?

WILLIAM C. DIX

OLD ENGLISH AIR

Moderato

What Child is this,— Who laid to rest — On Ma - ry's lap — is sleep - ing? What an - gels greet — with an - thems sweet, — While shep - herds watch — are keep - ing? This, this — is Christ the King; — Whom shep - herds guard — and an - gels sing: Haste, haste — to bring Him laud, — The Babe, the Son — of Ma - ry!

O Holy Night

ADOLPHE ADAM

41

HYMNS

Come, Thou Almighty King

CHARLES WESLEY

FELICE DE GIARDINI

Come, Thou al - might - y King, Help us Thy

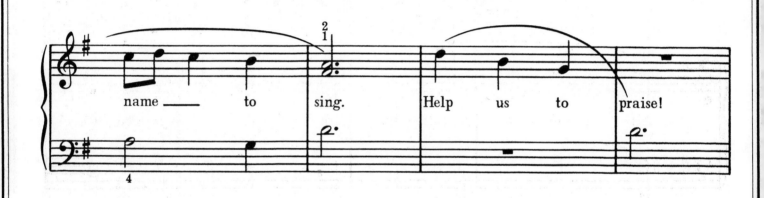

name ___ to sing. Help us to praise!

Fa - ther all glo - ri - ous, O'er all vic - to - ri - ous,

Come and reign o - ver us, An - cient of days.

Come Ye Thankful People, Come

HENRY ALFORD

GEORGE J. ELVEY

Moderato

mf Come, ye thank-ful peo-ple, come, Raise the song of har-vest home;

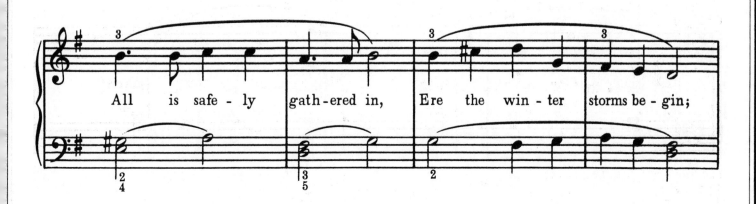

All is safe-ly gath-ered in, Ere the win-ter storms be-gin;

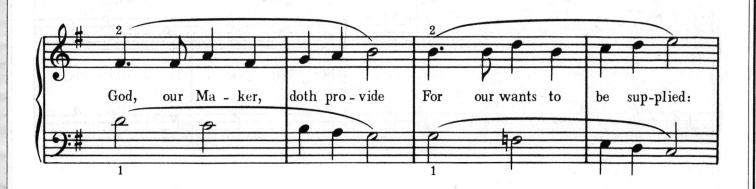

God, our Ma-ker, doth pro-vide For our wants to be sup-plied:

Come to God's own tem-ple, come, Raise the song of har-vest home.

Holy, Holy, Holy!

REGINALD HEBER

JOHN B. DYKES

With spirit

Ho - ly, Ho - ly, Ho - ly! Lord God Al - might - y!

Ear - ly in the morn - ing our song shall rise to Thee.

Ho - ly, Ho - ly, Ho - ly! Mer - ci - ful and Might - y,

God in Three Per - sons, bless - ed Trin - i - ty.

I Would Be True

HOWARD ARNOLD WALTER

JOSEPH YATES PEEK

mf I would be true for there are those who trust me;

I would be pure, for there are those who care;

I would be strong, for there is much to suf - fer;

I would be brave, for there is much to dare;

I would be brave, for there is much to dare.

Christ the Lord Is Risen Today

CHARLES WESLEY

EASTER HYMN

With spirit

mf Christ the Lord is ris'n to-day, — Al - le - lu - ia!

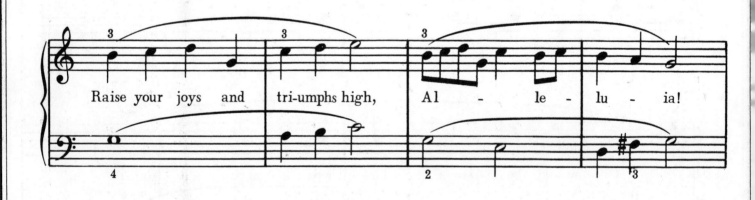

Sons of men and an-gels say: — Al - le - lu - ia!

Raise your joys and tri-umphs high, Al - le - lu - ia!

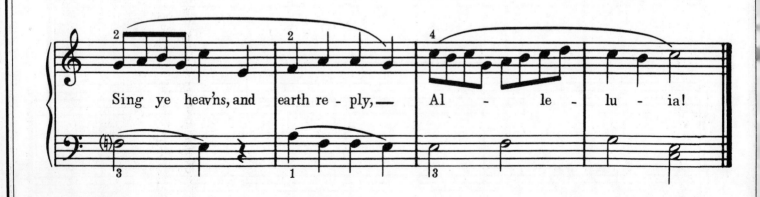

Sing ye heav'ns, and earth re - ply, — Al - le - lu - ia!

PATRIOTIC SONGS

The Battle Hymn of the Republic

JULIA WARD HOWE

WILLIAM STEFFE

Mine eyes have seen the glo-ry of the com-ing of the Lord. He is

tramp-ling out the vin-tage where the grapes of wrath are stored; He hath

loosed the fate-ful light-ning of His ter-ri-ble swift sword. His

truth is march-ing on!

Glo - ry! Glo - ry! Hal - le - lu - jah!

Glo - ry! Glo - ry! Hal - le - lu - jah!

Glo - ry! Glo - ry! Hal - le - lu - jah! His

truth is march - ing on!

The Yankee Doodle Boy

GEORGE M. COHAN

American Patrol

FRANK W. MEACHAM

Strict march time

2nd time to Coda

Stars and Stripes Forever

JOHN PHILIP SOUSA

des - pots re - mem - ber the day, _____ When our

fa - thers with might - y en - deav - or Pro -

claimed as they marched to the fray, _____ That by their

might, and by their right, It waves for ev - er.

The Star-Spangled Banner

FRANCIS SCOTT KEY

JOHN STAFFORD SMITH

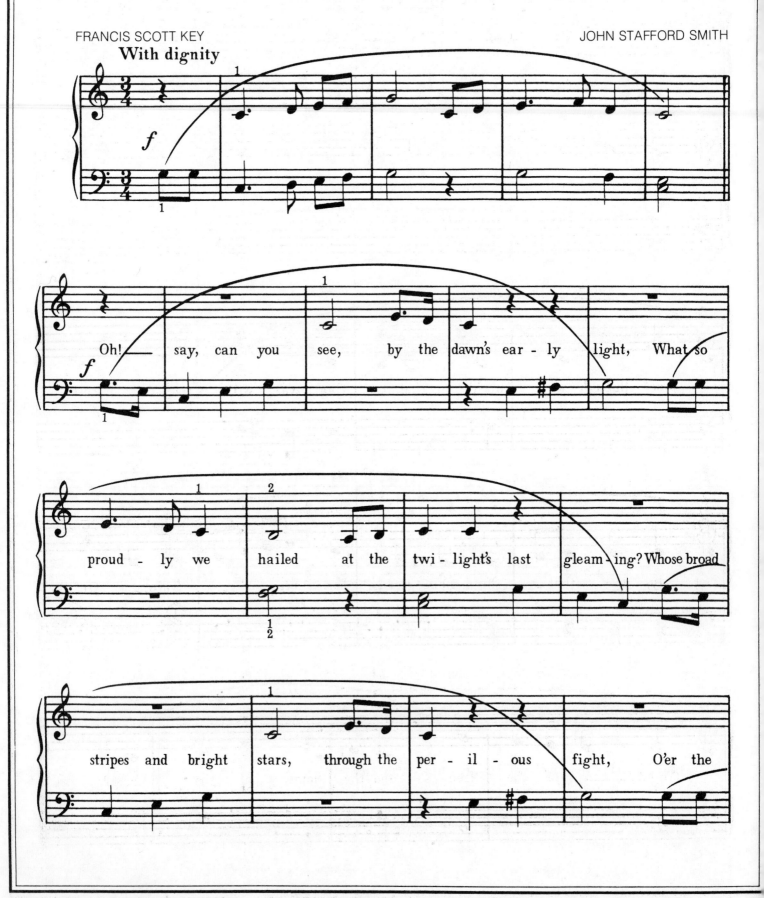

CLASSICS

Toreador Song

(from "Carmen")

GEORGES BIZET

Con spirito

Piano Concerto No. 2
(Theme from 3rd Movement)

SERGEI RACHMANINOFF

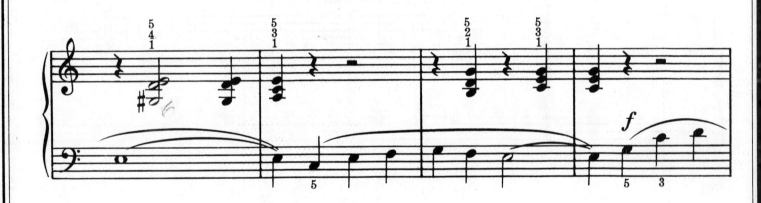

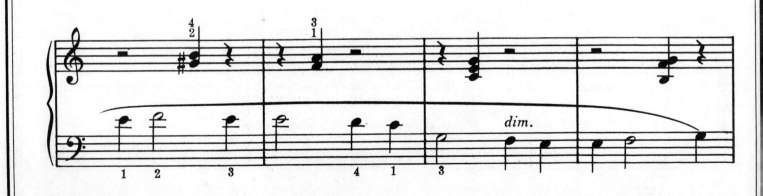

Fantaisie Impromptu

FREDERIC CHOPIN

Piano Concerto No. 1
(Theme from 1st Movement)

PETER TCHAIKOVSKY

"Pathetique" Symphony

(Theme from 1st Movement)

PETER TCHAIKOVSKY

Romeo and Juliet
(3rd Theme)

PETER TCHAIKOVSKY

Andante cantabile

Ave Maria

BACH/GOUNOD

The Swan
(from "Carnival of the Animals")

CAMILLE SAINT-SAËNS

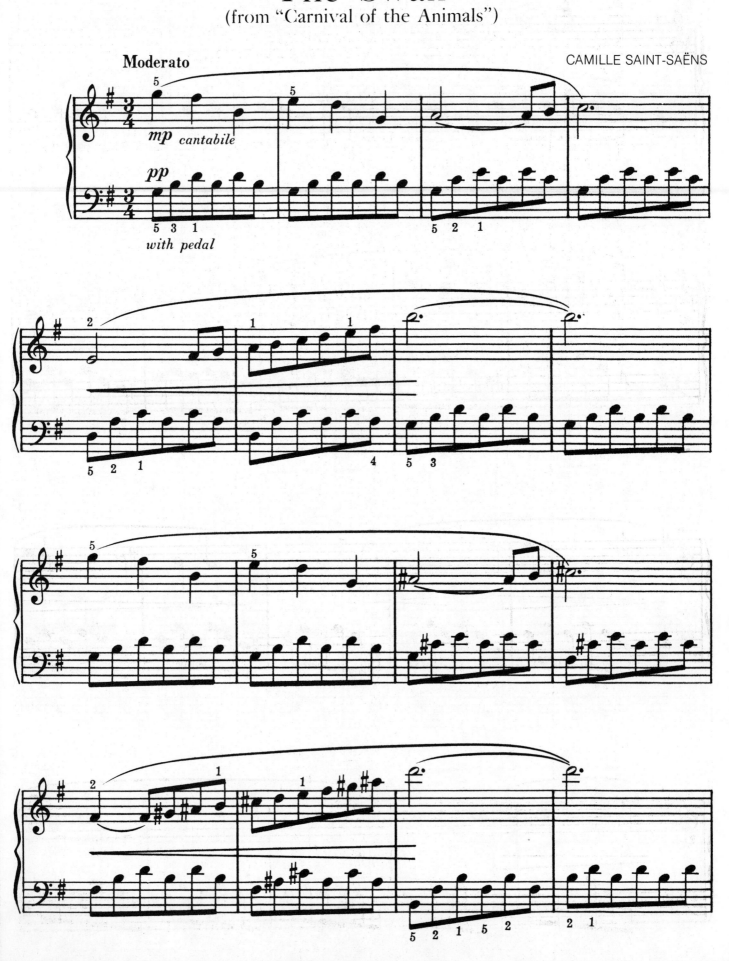

Liebestraum

FRANZ LISZT

cresc.   poco   a

poco   e   agitato

Waltzes

Merry Widow Waltz

Waltz time

FRANZ LEHAR

Mattinata

RUGGIERO LEONCAVALLO

Over the Waves

Waltz time

JUVENTINO ROSAS

Emperor Waltz

Waltz time

JOHANN STRAUSS

Fine

D. C. al Fine

Fascination

F. D. MARCHETTI

Waltz of the Flowers
(from "The Nutcracker Suite")

PETER TCHAIKOVSKY